It's Laugh O'Clock

Would You Rather?

Hugs and Kisses Edition

Funny Scenarios, Wacky Choices and Hilarious Situations For Kids and Family

With Fun Illustrations

Riddleland

Designs by freepik.com

TABLE OF CONTENTS

Riddleland Bonus

Join our **Facebook Group** at **Riddleland for Kids** to get daily jokes and riddles.

https://pixelfy.me/riddlelandbonus

Thank you for buying this book. As a token of our appreciation, we would like to offer a special bonus—a collection of 50 original jokes, riddles, and funny stories.

INTRODUCTION

"Love is in the Air... Or is that Bacon!"

Are you ready to make some decisions? ***Would You Rather? Hugs and Kisses Edition*** is a collection of funny scenarios, wacky choices, and hilarious situations which offer alternative endings for kids and adults to choose among.

These questions are an excellent way to get a fun and exciting conversation started. Also, by asking "Why?" after a "Would you Rather . . . " question, learn a lot about the person, including their values and their thinking process.

We wrote this book because we want children to be encouraged to read more, think, and grow. As parents, we know that when children play games, they are being educated while having so much fun that they don't even realize they're learning and developing valuable life skills. "Would you Rather . . . " is one of our favorite games to play as a family. Some of the 'would you rather ...' scenarios have had us in fits of giggles, others have generated reactions such as: "Eeeeeeuuugh, that's gross!" and yet others really make us think, reflect and consider our own decisions.

Besides having fun, playing these questions have other benefits such as:

Enhancing Communication – This game helps children to interact, read aloud, and listen to others. It's a fun way for parents to get their children interacting with them without a formal, awkward conversation. The game can also help to get to know someone better and learn about their likes, dislikes, and values.

Building Confidence – The game encourages children to get used to pronouncing vocabulary, asking questions, and overcoming shyness.

Developing Critical Thinking – It helps children to defend and justify the rationale for their choices and can generate discussions and debates. Parents playing this game with young children can give them prompting questions about their answers to help them reach logical and sensible decisions.

Improving Vocabulary – Children will be introduced to new words in the questions, and the context of them will help them remember the words because the game is fun.

Encouraging Equality and Diversity – Considering other people's answers, even if they differ from your own, is important for respect, equality, diversity, tolerance, acceptance, and inclusivity. Some questions may get children to think outside the box and move beyond stereotypes associated with gender.

Welcome to It's Laugh O'Clock

Would You Rather?
Hugs and Kisses Edition

How do you play?

At least two players are needed to play this game. Face your opponent and decide who is **Teddy 1** and **Teddy 2**. If you have 3 or 4 players, you can decide which players belong to **Group 1** and **Group 2**. The goal of the game is to score points by making the other players laugh. The first player to reach a score of 10 points is the **Round Champion**.

What are the rules?

Teddy 1 starts first. Read the questions aloud and choose an answer. The same player will then explain why they chose the answer in the silliest and wackiest way possible. If the reason makes **Teddy 2** laugh, then **Teddy 1** scores a funny point. Take turns going back and forth and write down the score.

How do you get started?

Flip a coin. The player that guesses it correctly starts first.

Bonus Tip:

Making funny voices, silly dance moves or wacky facial expressions will make your opponent laugh!

Most importantly:

Remember to have fun and enjoy the game!

Would You Rather...

Have giant wings and be able to fly
like Cupid

OR

make the most delicious caramel-filled chocolates
like the world's best candy maker?

Call your secret crush
"goober monkey boo boo schnookie wookums"

OR

have to kiss a stinky, muddy pig in front of everyone?

Would You Rather...

Write a poem for each member of your family that explains why you love them

make handmade valentines for every teacher at your school?

Receive an extra-special valentine from your favorite celebrity

from a member of the royal family?

Would You Rather...

Eat a slice of pizza
with heart-shaped pepperonis

French fries drizzled with
chocolate sauce?

Decorate for Valentine's Day by putting hundreds of red
roses in every single room of your house

by covering the walls of your classroom with poems
about the kids in your class?

Would You Rather...

Be surprised on Valentine's Day with a giant, talking teddy bear

with a whole room full of your favorite candy?

Cast a magic love spell to make your two favorite cartoon characters fall in love

your two favorite animals at the zoo fall in love?

Would You Rather...

eel loved on Valentine's Day by having your family hide notes
r you all over the house saying what they love most about you

OR

by doing all of your chores for you while you relax and watch your favorite TV show?

Play cards with the Queen of Hearts

OR

your favorite board game with Cupid?

Find out that your secret admirer is a goat covered with fleas

a spider who spits on all of your candy?

Go to a rodeo where all of the horses have bright red hair

to a carnival where all the rides are pink?

Wear pink knee socks with polka dot hearts over your pants

red tie-dyed, heart-shaped glasses to school for one month?

Accidentally misspell everyone's name while filling out valentines

accidentally mix up your valentines and give them to the wrong people?

Would You Rather...

Have Cupid deliver valentines to your class while wearing a humongous, red cowboy hat

while wearing a silly Hawaiian shirt?

Change Cupid`s dirty diapers for one month

hand wash all of St. Valentine's robes for one month?

Would You Rather...

Drink magic hot chocolate that makes you fall in love with an imaginary friend

that makes you yell "I love you" at the top of your lungs to everyone you see?

Go for a ride with your best friend on a giant swan boat

on a bicycle built for two?

Go to school with lipstick marks from grandma all over your face

with one of Cupid's arrows stuck in your right butt cheek?

Watch your favorite Valentine's Day movie

make up a Valentine's Day skit with your friends?

Would You Rather...

Impress your crush by teaching a dog how to bring them a rose

by telling them really funny jokes?

Shoot a bully with a magic arrow that makes them extra nice to everyone

have your teacher eat a magic cupcake that makes them give everyone in your class a homework pass?

Would You Rather...

Make up a Valentine's Day song and perform it live in front of a group of strangers at the mall

write a story about a frog who likes to kiss people and read it in front of your entire school?

Play cards against the Queen of Hearts

have an archery contest against Cupid?

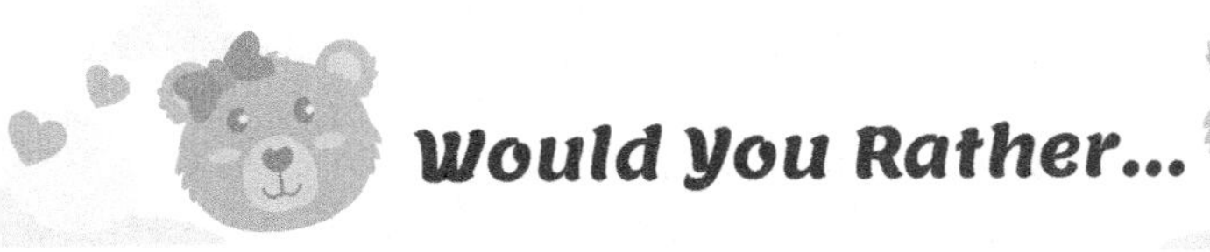

Would You Rather...

Have to wear silky boxer shorts

cherub wings over your clothes every time you play with your friends?

Have St. Valentine read you a story about the history of Valentine's Day

make up a story about falling in love with an armadillo?

Would You Rather...

Have your substitute teacher be Cupid

St. Valentine for a whole week?

Give valentines to your whole class that have your favorite animals on them and come with fruit snacks

that have your favorite superhero on them and come with stickers?

Would You Rather...

Open your lunchbox every day for one month to find a heart-shaped peanut butter and jelly sandwich

a love note from your parents?

Give your teacher a box of pink pencils

a basket of purple apples for Valentine's Day?

Would You Rather...

Have a pet pig who poops
heart-shaped candies

a duck who lays chocolate eggs?

Babysit adorable baby twin cherubs but
they keep having dirty diapers

take care of a colony of love bugs for one week, but you
have to feed them your Valentine's Day candy?

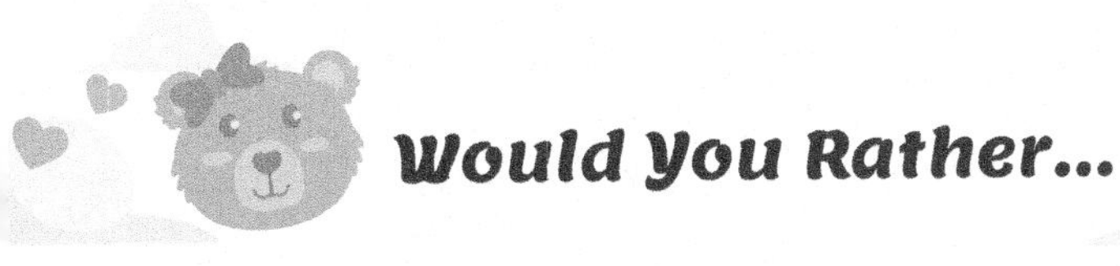

Pick flowers for your teacher

carry a rose in your teeth every day from now until Valentine's Day?

Bake cookies

hand-make valentines for every kid and teacher at your school?

Would You Rather...

Have Cupid hit you with a magic arrow that makes you sing every time you want to say something

that gives you really stinky breath?

Have a secret admirer who's so funny that they do stand-up comedy

who's so athletic that they can run a marathon?

Would You Rather...

Accidentally send all of your friends valentines that say, "you're my sweet little sugar bear,"

a text message that's just a bunch of emojis with heart eyes?

Get a huge teddy bear

a huge Valentine's Day card?

Would You Rather...

Go to a Valentine's Day party where you get to make your own valentine box

where you get to drink fruit punch out of fancy, crystal glasses?

Decorate cupcakes with pink and red sprinkles

decorate a cake with purple and white frosting?

Would You Rather...

Celebrate Valentine's Day by baking cookies with pink frosting for all of your neighbors

by giving a shiny red balloon to every kid at the park?

Wear only red and white clothes every day for one month

only write in pink pen every day for one month?

Would You Rather...

Decorate the inside of your house with thousands of handmade paper hearts

the outside of your house by drawing a giant, pink and red mural with sidewalk chalk?

Design a rainbow-colored wedding dress

a tie-dye print tuxedo?

Would You Rather...

Take a selfie with hearts painted all over your face

do a TikTok video with Cupid?

Get to watch the Valentine's Day episode of your favorite cartoon during class

get to watch your favorite Valentine's Day movie with your family at home?

Would You Rather...

Have it rain pink and red glitter

snow fluffy cotton candy puffs on Valentine's Day?

Play basketball with a heart-shaped ball that bounces unpredictably all over the place

using a pink paint ball, that gets paint on everything you touch for the rest of the day.

Write "XOXO"

"your secret admirer" after your name on all of your homework?

Give your crush a hug but they have really bad breath from eating stinky cheese

have your crush kiss you on the cheek, but they have really crusty lips that feel like sandpaper?

Would You Rather...

Have a Valentine's Day party at a waterpark with all your friends who wear pink swimsuits

in your room with all your stuffed animals who come to life?

Watch a romantic play with a group of your friends

a scary movie all by yourself?

Would You Rather...

Get in trouble with your parents for writing "be mine" on all of the walls in your house

get in trouble with your teacher for eating all of their Valentine's chocolate?

Make embarrassing animal noises

have really bad gas every time your crush is around?

Would You Rather...

Have St. Valentine teach you all about the history of Valentine's Day

have a sorceress teach you how to make a love potion?

Go to the zoo on Valentine's Day to hand-feed pink and red birds

to give zoo guests a tutorial about how to hug gorillas?

Would you Rather...

Celebrate Valentine's Day for one month and get a new valentine everyday

celebrate St. Patrick's Day for one month and have good luck every day?

Have your parents call you a really embarrassing, silly pet-name in front of your friends

completely ignore you in front of your friends?

Would You Rather...

Get bit by a love bug who makes you say nice things to everyone you meet

shot by Cupid's arrow that makes you like someone you're not friends with in class?

Visit Cupid's secret cloud fort

the Goddess of Love's magic temple?

Would You Rather...

Go to a movie and wear 3D glasses that make it look like hearts are popping off of the screen

eat pink popcorn that tastes like candy hearts?

Have your parents read you a story about how much they love you

write a story about how much you love your family?

Would You Rather...

Wear a T-shirt that smells like chocolate

a T-shirt that smells like fancy perfume?

Go to a Valentine's Day ball where you dress up in fancy clothes and eat pink cupcakes

to a Valentine's Day BBQ where you wear comfy clothes and eat heart-shaped hamburgers?

Would You Rather...

Have to eat a whole box of chocolates filled with the yuckiest flavor you've ever tasted

pick up thousands of pieces of white and red confetti after a Valentine's Day party?

See Cupid wear a pink Hawaiian shirt

a tuxedo T-shirt with his diaper?

Would You Rather...

Stand in the middle of a big city on Valentine's Day and offer free hugs to everyone you see

pass out red roses to everyone you see?

Make all your valentines in a secret fort in the middle of the woods

in an art studio in a busy city?

Would You Rather...

Make valentines for all your friends out of fresh produce from the grocery store

out of rocks and flowers you find in the forest?

Make all your friends origami roses

buy all your friends friendship bracelets for Valentine's Day?

Would You Rather...

Show your family you love them on Valentine's Day by making them breakfast in bed every day for a week

by doing all their chores for a day?

Look up in the sky and see a flock of birds flying in the shape of a heart

a hot air balloon shaped like a teddy bear?

Would You Rather...

Be a gourmet chocolatier at a candy shop
the week of Valentine's Day

an expert florist at a flower shop
the week of Valentine's Day?

Give your friends valentines with red glitter that
gets all over their clothes

with fuzzy stickers that get stuck to their fingers?

Would You Rather...

Have purple skin for one month

pink teeth for one month?

Host a Valentine's Day party at an enchanted toy store where all the teddy bears come to life to play with you and your friends

be a guest at a Valentine's Day party at a candy store where your bag keeps magically refilling with your favorite treats?

Would You Rather...

Practice self-love by looking in the mirror and loudly shouting all the things you like about yourself

by relaxing and playing with your favorite bath toys in a tub full of cotton candy-flavored bubbles?

Send valentines to all your friends via email

by hand-delivering them?

Would You Rather...

Accidentally give your crush a heart-shaped box full of vegetables instead of chocolates

a valentine full of itching powder instead of glitter?

Send a valentine to someone in the future

find an old valentine from someone in the past?

Would You Rather...

Take a vacation where you get to stay at Cupid's cloud castle in the sky

where you get to stay in a hotel made entirely out of chocolate that you can eat?

Eat a rose-petal sandwich

a chocolate-covered onion?

Would You Rather...

Plant a garden full of red roses that smell like macaroni and cheese

full of pink posies that smell like brownies?

Take pictures with your friends in a candy store full of red, pink, and white candies

in a huge field of purple flowers?

Would You Rather...

Hug all your friends on Valentine's Day with tiny, green T-rex arms

with long, hairy orangutan arms?

Work at a wedding as the head chef who bakes a delicious, 10-tiered wedding cake

as the DJ who plays the best dance songs all night long?

Would You Rather...

Take a selfie with a filter that gives you orange heart eyes

purple cupid wings?

Go to school on Valentine's day with one half of your face painted red and the other half painted white

with a giant pink wig that looks like cotton candy?

Would You Rather...

Be Cupid for a day but have giant wings that get stuck in every doorway you walk through

have a diaper that's two sizes too small, so you have a wedgie all day?

Have to kiss a slimy snake

hug a prickly porcupine?

Would You Rather...

Only be able to color with purple crayons
or markers for the rest of your life

only be able to eat red food for
the rest of your life?

Go to a concert to watch your favorite celebrity
sing love songs

to be the celebrity on stage singing love songs?

Would You Rather...

Give all your friends valentines that play really annoying love songs when they open them

valentines that pop messy, rainbow confetti when they open them?

Kiss an extra-spicy jalapeño

hug a tiny cactus?

Accidentally fall asleep in class and shout your crush's name over and over again

have your parents come to class to give you a kiss in front of everyone?

Have red lipstick all over your face

pink paint all over your hair?

Would You Rather...

See Cupid trade his bow and arrows for a slingshot that shoots candy hearts

a water gun that shoots fruit punch?

Have magic powers that give you the ability to make flowers grow really quickly

the ability to make people who don't get along like each other?

Would You Rather...

Get nervous around your crush
and accidentally throw up on them

accidentally blurt out your
most embarrassing secret in front of them?

Make friendship bracelets for all your
friends and family

eat an entire a box of Valentine's chocolates
all by yourself?

Would You Rather...

Have a Valentine's Day party in an underground cave with all your friends

in a secret treehouse with your family?

Get a valentine from someone you love very much

get lots of valentine from other kids who live in countries all over the world?

Spend Valentine's Day at the zoo and see a giraffe with heart-shaped spots

a giant tortoise that poops chocolate candies?

Have to toss rose petals everywhere you go

wear red, polka-dotted underwear over your pants for a whole day?

Would You Rather...

Take a submarine deep underwater to deliver valentines to a city of mermaids

take a rocket ship to a lost planet to deliver candy hearts to friendly aliens?

Hold hands with an octopus

snuggle with a crocodile?

Would You Rather...

Travel back in time to celebrate Valentine's Day with plant-eating dinosaurs who feast on heart-shaped leaves

into the future to celebrate Valentine's Day with rusty robots who like to sing love songs?

Get kisses from an Aunt with bad breath

from a really slobbery dog?

Would You Rather...

Cut 1,000 thorny roses

eat 1,000 pieces of yucky candy?

Get in trouble for sneaking chocolate and not be allowed to eat any more candy for the next month

for texting your crush in class and have to read your message out loud in front of everyone?

Would You Rather...

See Cupid wear a fluffy pink tutu

a plaid red kilt instead of his traditional diaper?

Go to a Valentine's Day birthday party at a trampoline park where heart-shaped balloons fall from the ceiling

to a Valentine's Day slumber party at Cupid's house where you get to sleep on a cloud?

Walk around all day holding a bouquet of flowers that has bugs crawling all over it

with a chocolate stain on your pants that everyone thinks is poo?

Have glittery, pink teeth

a hairy, purple tongue?

Would You Rather...

Trade all of your valentines for a cute new kitten

a free pass to not do your chores for one month?

Hide chocolate kisses around your classroom for your friends to find

have your teacher give you a box of candy hearts?

Would You Rather...

Be able to eat as much chocolate as you want on Valentine's Day without getting sick

get a card from every single person you know that says what they like about you?

Wear silky socks that make you slip around

velvety socks that make your feet sweat?

Would You Rather...

Have to wear a temporary tattoo on your forehead that says, “I love you” for one week

get a real tattoo on your arm that says, “I love myself?”

Have your teacher smash a pink cupcake in your face in front of the whole class

paint your skin red for one week?

Would You Rather...

See your teacher dress like Cupid and wear wings, a diaper, and a sash

give a whole box of chocolates to each kid in your class on Valentine's Day?

Never be able to eat candy ever again

never be able to hug your friends ever again?

Have Cupid's arrows make people
sing silly songs

do funny dances?

Go deep under the ocean and blow heart-shaped bubbles
with mermaids who can talk to fish

visit outer space and play with Martians who can turn
meteors into candy?

Would You Rather...

Plant a rose bush that grows candy roses

a palm tree that grows chocolate coconuts?

Use your screen time to make silly TikTok videos to your favorite love songs

to watch helpful YouTube tutorials about how to make awesome valentines for your friends?

Get a basket of your favorite snacks

a basket of silly joke books instead of candy on Valentine's Day?

Get a paper cut from every valentine you fill out

accidentally sit on a rose bush with sharp thorns?

Only be able to wear itchy pink and red clothes for a week

only be able to eat candy that gives you a stomachache for a week?

Have your heart beat loud enough that everyone in your house can hear it

pucker your lips at school for a day?

Would You Rather...

Have your armpits smell like roses

have your feet smell like chocolate?

Wish all of your friends and family a happy Valentine's Day by handmaking valentines for each of them

by having hour-long Zoom calls with each of them?

Would You Rather...

Get a paper cut every time you make a paper heart

get a toothache every time you eat a piece of candy?

Learn about different Valentine's Day customs around the world

visit one country of your choice on Valentine's Day?

Would You Rather...

Read a love story about two dogs who get married at the beach

a spooky mystery about a bandit who keeps stealing people's valentines?

Give funny valentines to all of your friends

a mushy valentine to one person who is very special to you?

Would You Rather...

Exercise by jumping 50 times on a heart-shaped trampoline with extra-bouncy springs

by carrying 50 boxes of chocolate from one end of the candy shop to the other?

Receive flowers that smell like poo

chocolates that have yucky-flavored filling?

Would You Rather...

Give 1,000 roses to your friends

eat 1,000 pieces of candy?

Have to put little hearts instead of dots on all of your "i"s and "j"s for the rest of the school year

tell your teacher "I love you" in front of the whole class every day for the rest of the school year?

Would You Rather...

Surprise your teacher on Valentine's Day by filling your classroom with purple balloons

by filling their desk with big bouquets of red flowers?

Make valentines in your room and accidentally spill glitter everywhere

make valentines at school and accidentally glue your hand to your desk?

Would You Rather...

Celebrate Valentine's Day in the summer and have a pool party with the water dyed pink

in the winter and have a snowball fight with heart-shaped snowballs?

Accidentally celebrate Valentine's Day one day early

forget to celebrate it?

Would You Rather...

Have to eat all your Valentine's Day candy
with a fork and knife

only get one, big candy bar but you have
to eat it in one bite?

Wear a jeweled crown that makes your hair grow
all the way down to the floor

a gold bracelet that turns your skin bright pink?

Would You Rather...

Join a rock band as the lead singer who
only sings love songs

as the bass player who has a heart-shaped guitar?

Give your best friend a cute new puppy

a valentine that dispenses a candy bar
every time they open it?

Would You Rather...

Get a kiss from a spiky blowfish who pokes you

from a super strong gorilla who squeezes you tightly?

Cook a big, fancy Valentine's Day dinner for your friends

clean up after a Valentine's Day pizza party for your class?

Would You Rather...

Drink purple soda that makes you burp loudly

pink apple juice that gives you hiccups?

Have your friends play a prank on you by drawing a mustache on your face in red, permanent marker

by replacing all your candy hearts with tiny pieces of chalk?

Would You Rather...

Go camping on Valentine's Day in a cabin that smells like sugar cookies

in a tent that's made out of chocolate?

Be driven to school on Valentine's Day in really fast, pink race car

in a fancy carriage pulled by a purple unicorn?

Would You Rather...

Celebrate Valentine's Day with your family
by making a nice dinner for them

by drawing special pictures for them?

Have to do a silly dance every time
you hug someone

have to shout, "I have stinky feet!" every time
you eat a piece of candy?

Would You Rather...

Serenade your crush by playing their favorite song on the tuba

by singing your favorite song at the top of your lungs?

Get a hall pass to pass out valentines to kids in other classes

to deliver candy grams to all of the teachers in your grade?

Would You Rather...

Go to a dog wedding at the park

to a zebra wedding at the zoo?

Start a new Valentine's Day tradition where you wake up early and eat heart-shaped pancakes

stay up late and eat strawberry-flavored popsicles?

Would You Rather...

Go on a 16-hour flight that only plays romantic movies with lots of hugging

on a road trip with your family, but the radio only plays sappy love ballads?

Be a jeweler who makes wedding rings

a geologist who studies precious gemstones?

Receive one dozen vanilla cupcakes

one dozen purple roses?

Celebrate Valentine's Day by going to a fireworks show that has pink and purple fireworks

by going to an ice cream shop with red and white ice cream?

Would You Rather...

Eat so much candy that you get a cavity and have to make a special trip to the dentist

drink so much hot chocolate that you have to go to the bathroom every 10 minutes for a whole day?

Receive purple flowers that smell like waffles

chocolate candy that tastes like bacon?

Laugh uncontrollably

cry uncontrollably every time you see your crush?

Go to couples' therapy with an angry dinosaur who spits when they talk

on a dinner date with a hairy monkey who throws dinner rolls at other customers?

Would You Rather...

Have your secret admirer send you 1 dozen donuts

a new toy?

Give your friends and family valentines at every holiday for the rest of the year

give your friends and family valentines every single day for one month?

Would You Rather...

Give everyone in your class a giant candy bar

have everyone in your class give you
a tiny candy bar?

Paint a Valentine's Day mural
on a wall at your school

write a short love story that you get to read
to the whole school?

Eat chocolate sushi

a flower sandwich?

Show your friends you love them by letting them borrow your favorite toys for one week

by giving them the best part of your lunch every day for one week?

Would You Rather...

Compete in your school's talent show by doing
a science experiment with flowers

by doing a dance while dressed like Cupid?

Enter your school's talent show to do
a fancy ballroom dance

to play your favorite love song on the piano?

Would You Rather...

Have your teacher give you a valentine with a homework pass inside

a valentine with a gift card to your favorite store inside?

Relax by taking a bubble bath with candy-scented bubbles

by rereading all your valentines?

Would You Rather...

Celebrate Valentine's Day by having a barbecue with heart-shaped hamburgers

by planting a garden full of different-colored roses?

Go to a school dance dressed in a red tuxedo with a lacy bowtie

in a purple dress with heart-shaped polka dots?

Would You Rather...

Get a valentine that squirts you in the face with water when you open it

that sets off a stink bomb when you open it?

Wear red polka-dotted footy pajamas to school every day for one month

really stinky cologne or perfume to school every day for one month?

Would You Rather...

Have your tongue get puffy from licking too many envelopes

have your hand get sore from writing too many valentines?

Trade all of your Valentine's Day candy for cupcakes made with salt instead of sugar

for a book full of math worksheets?

Would You Rather...

Accidentally give all of your friends
Christmas cards

birthday cards instead of valentines?

Make heart-shaped treats for every dog
at the animal shelter

make pink and red cupcakes for all of the grandparents
at the retirement home?

Would You Rather...

Be a wedding officiant who accidentally sneezes in the middle of the ceremony

a wedding guest who eats too much cake and gets a stomachache?

Decorate your bedroom with bright red wallpaper

with a huge poster of the Queen of Hearts?

Would You Rather...

Star in a movie as the main character
of a romantic comedy

as the villain of a horror film?

Take a cruise on a love boat that has a giant,
heart-shaped water slide

take a ride on a red train that transports valentines
across the country?

Would You Rather...

Take a shower in water that smells like strawberry milkshakes

a bath with rubber ducks that quack love songs?

Babysit cherub triplets who need you to change their dirty diapers

take care of your class pet who eats all your Valentine's Day candy?

Would You Rather...

Get married in space where you “kiss” while wearing astronaut suits and helmets

at the bottom of the ocean where you “kiss” while wearing scuba masks and tanks?

Visit an aquarium
to see a kissing fish exhibit

visit a zoo to feed the love birds?

Go swimming in a heart-shaped pool

sleep on a heart-shaped bed?

Pick 1,000 roses without getting
poked by any thorns

eat 1,000 candy hearts without getting
a stomachache?

Would You Rather...

Deliver valentines to all your friends while riding on a sparkly pink skateboard

while riding on a white horse with a red mane?

Trim the thorns off a field-full of roses before they're given as Valentine's Day gifts

plant a field full of flowers after Valentine's Day?

Have a snowball fight with snowballs made of purple cotton candy

a mud fight with mud made of chocolate?

Get bit by a love bug and fall in love with the next person you see

have a love bird follow you around because it wants you to be its mate?

Did You Enjoy The Book ?

If you did, we are ecstatic. If not, please write your complaint to us and we will ensure we fix it.

If you're feeling generous, there is something important that you can help me with – tell other people that you enjoyed the book.

Ask a grown-up to write about it on Amazon. When they do, more people will find out about the book. It also lets Amazon know that we are making kids around the world laugh. Even a few words and ratings would go a long way.

If you have any ideas or jokes that you think are super funny, please let us know. We would love to hear from you.

Our email address is -

riddleland@riddlelandforkids.com

Riddleland Bonus

Join our **Facebook Group** at **Riddleland for Kids** to get daily jokes and riddles.

https://pixelfy.me/riddlelandbonus

Thank you for buying this book. As a token of our appreciation, we would like to offer a special bonus—a collection of 50 original jokes, riddles, and funny stories.

CONTEST

Would you like your jokes and riddles to be featured in our next book?

We are having a contest to discover the cleverest and funniest boys and girls in the world!

1) Creative and Challenging Riddles
2) Tickle Your Funny Bone Contest

Parents, please email us your child's "original" riddle or joke. He or she could win a Riddleland book and be featured in our next book.

Here are the rules:

1) We're looking for super challenging riddles and extra funny jokes.

2) Jokes and riddles MUST be 100% original—NOT something discovered on the Internet.

3) You can submit both a joke and a riddle because they are two separate contests.

4) Don't get help from your parents—UNLESS they're as funny as you are.

5) Winners will be announced via email or our Facebook group – **Riddleland for kids**

6) In your entry, please confirm which book you purchased.

Email us at **Riddleland@riddlelandforkids.com**

Other Fun Books by Riddleland

Riddles Series

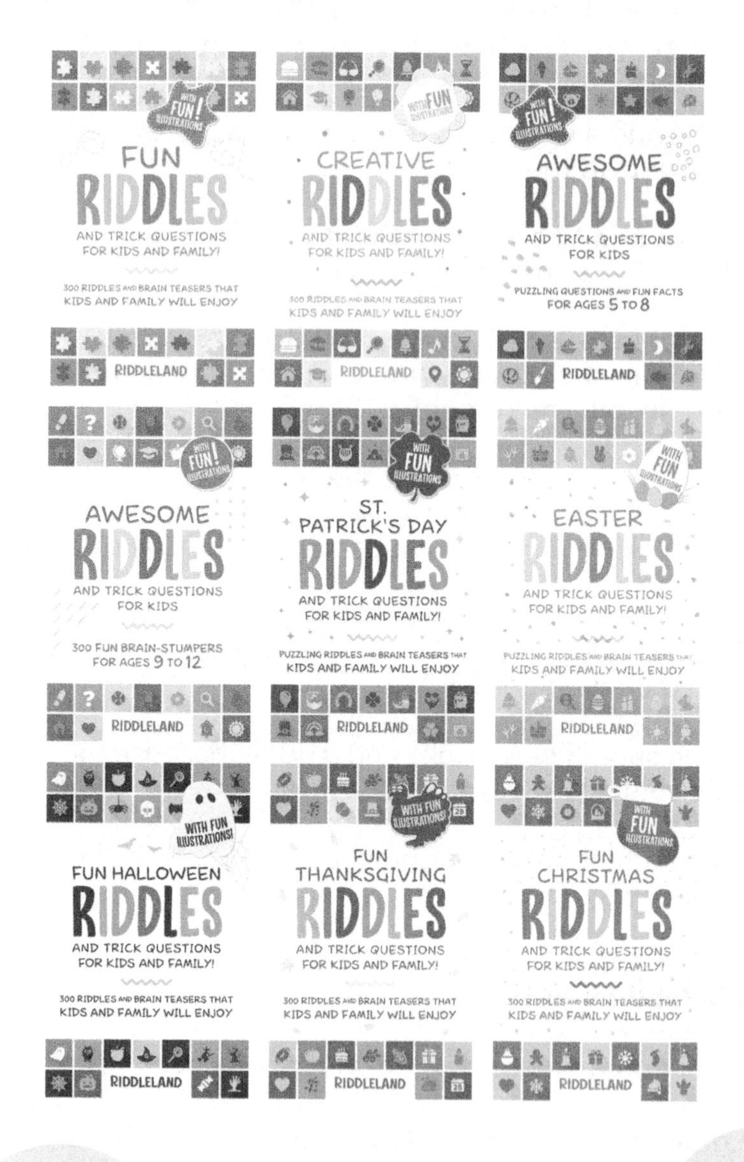

It's Laugh O'Clock Joke Books

Would You Rather...Series

Get them on Amazon or our website at

www.riddlelandforkids.com

ABOUT RIDDLELAND

Riddleland is a mum + dad run publishing company. We are passionate about creating fun and innovative books to help children develop their reading skills and fall in love with reading. If you have suggestions for us or want to work with us, shoot us an email at

riddleland@riddlelandforkids.com

Our favourite family quote

"Creativity is an area in which younger people have a tremendous advantage since they have an endearing habit of always questioning past wisdom and authority."

– *Bill Hewlett*

Made in the USA
Monee, IL
04 February 2022